Graphic Chillers

DRACULA

Bram Stoker • Daniel Conner • Rod Espinosa

Graphic Chillers

FRANKENSTEIN

Mary Shelley • Elizabeth Genco • Jason Ho

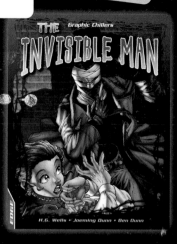

Graphic Chillers

THE INVISIBLE MAN

H.G. Wells • Joeming Dunn • Ben Dunn

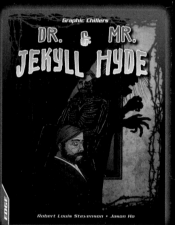

Graphic Chillers

DR. & MR. JEKYLL HYDE

Robert Louis Stevenson • Jason Ho

Graphic Chillers

THE LEGEND OF SLEEPY HOLLOW

Washington Irving • Jeff Zornow

Graphic Chillers

MUMMY

Bram Stoker • Bart A. Thompson • Brian Miroglio

Graphic Chillers

THE PHANTOM OF THE OPERA

Gaston Leroux • Joeming Dunn • Rod Espinosa

Graphic Chillers

WEREWOLF

Jeff Zornow

MUMMY

ABOUT THE AUTHOR

Bram Stoker was born in Dublin, Ireland, on 8 November, 1847. He was the third of seven children. Stoker was ill throughout his childhood, and as a result he did not walk until he was seven years old.

Stoker outgrew his illness, and began to study at Trinity College, Dublin when he was 16. He became an outstanding athlete. While he was a student, he discovered a passion for theatre.

In 1870, Stoker began his work as a civil servant at Dublin Castle. In 1878, he met his idol, actor Sir Henry Irving. He soon accepted a job as Irving's manager.

Stoker first published his novel *Jewel of the Seven Stars* (on which this graphic novel is based) in 1903. It was made into several film adaptations, including Hammer's *Blood from the Mummy's Tomb* in 1971, and director Jeffrey Obrow's *Bram Stoker's Legend of the Mummy* in 1997.

Stoker wrote several novels, including his most famous one, *Dracula*, before his death on 20 April, 1912, in London.

Graphic Chillers

MUMMY

ADAPTED BY
BART A. THOMPSON

ILLUSTRATED BY
BRIAN MIROGLIO

BASED UPON THE WORKS OF
BRAM STOKER

EDGE
FRANKLIN WATTS

LONDON·SYDNEY

EGYPT 1967.
VALLEY OF THE SORCERER.
A TOMB HAS BEEN FOUND...

YAAAAAAAAHHHHHHHH!

MISTER?

MISTER?
YOU ALRIGHT?

YAAAAAAAAADHHHHHHH!

PRESENT DAY.
MARIN COUNTY, CALIFORNIA.

ABEL TRELAWNEY'S STUDY.

MRRROOWWRRR

NOT NOW, SILVIA. GO AWAY.

EXPRESS

AH, YES...THERE WE ARE.

WE CALL UPON THY POWERS TO RESTORE LIFE...

...NO...

I WON'T DO IT!

WHAT'S THIS?

NO! NO! NOOO!

SHCKA SHCKA

ALRIGHT, BUDDY!

WHO ARE YOU AND WHY ARE YOU BREAKING INTO MY PLACE?!

MISS TRELAWNY SENT ME! SHE SAID SHE CALLED YOU!

BEEP BEEP

ROBERT? IT'S MARGARET.

I KNOW WE HAVEN'T SPOKEN IN A WHILE, BUT I NEED YOUR HELP.

REALLY? LET'S SEE ABOUT THAT...

SOMETHING TERRIBLE HAS HAPPENED TO MY FATHER. I'M SENDING HIS DRIVER FOR YOU.

I'LL UNDERSTAND IF YOU DON'T WANT TO COME, BUT I HOPE YOU WILL.

YEAH. OKAY, LET'S GO.

PERHAPS MR. TRELAWNEY HIMSELF CAN GIVE US A BIT OF HELP ON THE IDENTITY OF HIS ATTACKER.

MR. WYATT, PLEASE.

HOW COULD HE POSSIBLY DO SUCH A THING IN HIS STATE?

IT SEEMS HE WAS RECORDING HIMSELF AT THE TIME.

MARGARET, I'M ON THE VERGE OF A DISCOVERY.

IF FOR SOME REASON I AM SUDDENLY STRICKEN DOWN, BY ACCIDENT OR ATTACK, YOU MUST FOLLOW MY INSTRUCTIONS TO THE LETTER.

I MUST REMAIN IN MY STUDY, BUT NEVER LEFT ALONE. DAY AND NIGHT AT LEAST TWO PERSONS MUST REMAIN IN THE ROOM.

NONE OF THE EGYPTIAN ARTEFACTS CAN BE MOVED. THERE IS A SPECIAL PURPOSE IN THE PLACEMENT OF EACH PIECE. ALSO, THE SMALL KEY MUST REMAIN ON MY WRIST.

MY LIFE WILL BE IN YOUR HANDS.

HEY, DOC. DO YOU KNOW WHAT THIS KEY OPENS?

NO IDEA.

MRRROOWWRRR

NOT NOW, SILVIA. GO AWAY.

I WON'T DO IT!

NO! NO! NOOO!

LATER, IN THE GUEST ROOM.

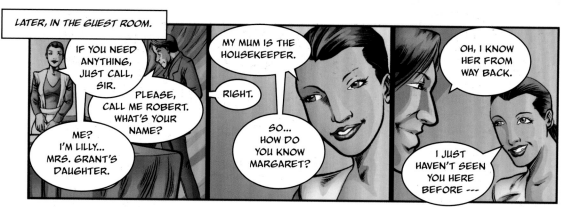

IF YOU NEED ANYTHING, JUST CALL, SIR.

PLEASE, CALL ME ROBERT. WHAT'S YOUR NAME?

ME? I'M LILLY... MRS. GRANT'S DAUGHTER.

MY MUM IS THE HOUSEKEEPER.

RIGHT.

SO... HOW DO YOU KNOW MARGARET?

OH, I KNOW HER FROM WAY BACK.

I JUST HAVEN'T SEEN YOU HERE BEFORE ---

BUT THEN THIS HOUSE GIVES ME THE CREEPS!

IT HAS ITS OWN PERSONALITY. IT MAKES STRANGE NOISES... ESPECIALLY THAT STUDY.

LATE ONE NIGHT WHEN MR. TRELAWNEY WAS ALREADY IN BED ASLEEP, THE DOOR WAS OPEN JUST A CRACK AND I HEARD A NOISE AND SAW LIGHTS DIMMING. I STARTED TO PEEK MY HEAD IN WHEN ---

MRRRROOOWWWRR!!!

HISSSSSSS!!!

SORRY ROBERT. I HAVE TO GO.

WAIT! WHAT DID YOU SEE?

IT'S SUPPOSED TO RAIN TONIGHT. YOU MIGHT WANT TO CLOSE THE SHUTTERS BEFORE YOU GO TO BED.

AH... OKAY.

SO... THERE ARE STABLES ON THE PROPERTY. I HAVEN'T HEARD HORSES THE WHOLE TIME I'VE BEEN HERE.

THERE ARE NO HORSES ANYMORE.

MR. TRELAWNEY GAVE THEM AWAY A FEW MONTHS BACK.

THAT'S A SHAME.

LILLY, COULD YOU HAVE THE HEAT TURNED UP?

I'LL GET YOU ANOTHER HEATER FROM THE BASEMENT.

THANKS.

9

ROBERT GOES OUT TO THE STABLES.

HMM... WHAT'S THIS?

WHACK!!!

IN THE TRELAWNEY HOUSE BASEMENT.

LILLY! WHERE HAVE YOU GONE?

I'M JUST FETCHING MR. WYATT A HEATER MUM!

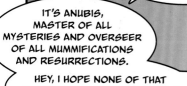

IN THE STUDY, ROBERT BEGINS TO FALL ASLEEP.

HRRRRRR...

HUUUHHH

HUH? WHAT'S WRONG?

SLAM

HRRRRRR...

N-N-NOOOOO!

MRS. GRANT!

AAAAAAHHHHHHH!!!

CARL! WHAT'S HAPPENING?

I'M LEAVING, MISS.

ALONG WITH MOST OF THE HOUSE STAFF.

AFTER THE FRIGHT MRS. GRANT HAD LAST NIGHT, I HOPE THAT SHE AND LILLY LEAVE, TOO.

STRANGE THINGS HAVE HAPPENED IN THIS HOUSE OVER THE LAST FEW YEARS. THIS WAS JUST TOO MUCH.

BUT MY FATHER NEEDS YOU NOW!

PLEASE DON'T GO...

KEEPING THE POLICE OUT OF THIS IS GROWING MORE DIFFICULT. SOMEONE IS OBVIOUSLY TRYING TO KILL YOUR FATHER.

HAVE THERE BEEN ANY STRANGERS AROUND, UNUSUAL CALLS, OR ANYTHING LIKE THAT?

NOT THAT I CAN REMEMBER... BUT THERE WAS SOMEONE FATHER WAS EXPECTING WHO NEVER SHOWED UP.

SOMEONE?

HE WAS VERY UPSET, BUT THEN A PACKAGE CAME AND HE WAS CALM AGAIN.

WHAT WAS THE NAME?

IT WAS...COR... CORBIN...?

CORBECK?!

THAT'S IT! JOHN CORBECK!

A DREADFUL MAN! A LIAR, THIEF, AND A GRAVE ROBBER...

AH, C'MON DOYLE. TELL US WHAT YOU REALLY THINK...

WE'RE FORTUNATE THAT MAN HASN'T SET FOOT IN THIS HOUSE!

LET'S SEE WHAT WE HAVE HERE...

J. Corbeck
555-7258

GOTCHA!

THE OFFICE OF BRYCE RENARD.

OKAY, FROM 1967 IT SEEMS EVERYTHING IN TRELAWNEY'S STUDY

IS FROM THE TOMB OF QUEEN TERA. IT'S ALL IN HIS LOG...

BUT NONE OF IT HAS BEEN SEEN SINCE.

WHY NOT?

YOU KNOW, I WAS IN THIS TOMB YEARS AGO. SOME OF THE ITEMS HAVEN'T BEEN TOUCHED.

QUEEN TERA'S DYING BREATH WAS A CURSE FOR TOUCHING ANYTHING. YOU'RE CURSED FOR EVEN TALKING ABOUT WHAT YOU'VE SEEN.

WHICH I HAVEN'T UNTIL NOW...

DRRRRRR-TTTT

AKK... AKKKTTTKKK... AAKKGGRR...

IT'S ROBERT. OKAY? YEAH.

PLEASE.

I'M LOOKING FOR JOHN CORBECK.

THANKS.

THE ASYLUM.

JOHN CORBECK? MY NAME IS ROBERT WYATT.

I'M HERE FOR ABEL TRELAWNEY.

I'M NOT INTERESTED SON.

WELL, I'M IN HERE *BECAUSE* OF ABEL TRELAWNEY.

BUT MARGARET SAID YOU WERE SUPPOSED TO COME BY THE HOUSE.

YEAH, YOU SENT THE PACKAGE HE WAS WAITING FOR, DIDN'T YOU?

MARGARET IS AT THE HOUSE?

I SENT MANY PACKAGES TO ABEL TRELAWNEY OVER THE YEARS.

LOOK, ABEL TRELAWNEY IS IN A *COMA*.

WHAT?!

HE WAS ATTACKED, BUT WE DON'T KNOW WHO DID IT.

WERE THERE ANY MARKS ON HIM? LIKE SEVEN SCRATCHES ON HIS WRIST OR NECK, SIDE-BY-SIDE?

HOW DID YOU KNOW...?!

YOU MUST TAKE ME THERE AT ONCE!

I'D LIKE TO BUT THERE'S THE SLIGHT PROBLEM OF ALL THIS...

MR. WYATT, I'M NOT IN HERE BECAUSE PEOPLE THINK I'M CRAZY...

...I'M IN HERE BECAUSE *I* THINK I'M CRAZY.

NOW WE MUST HURRY. EVERYONE IN THAT HOUSE IS IN *DANGER!* ESPECIALLY MARGARET!

17

NOW.

ON THAT LAST EXPEDITION WITH ABEL, WE TRAVELLED TO THE VALLEY OF THE SORCERER WHERE WE DISCOVERED THE TOMB OF THE MOST POWERFUL WOMAN IN ALL OF EGYPT: QUEEN TERA MOSEF.

BUT SHE WAS A BIT TOO POWERFUL.

THE PRIESTS WERE GOING TO HAVE HER KILLED BECAUSE SHE WAS A RISK TO THEIR AUTHORITY.

THAT IS THE OFFICIAL STORY.

THE TRUTH IS SHE HEARD OF THE PLOT AGAINST HER LIFE AND CAME UP WITH A PLAN TO HAVE HERSELF MUMMIFIED.

WEREN'T ALL ROYALTY MUMMIFIED BACK THEN?

YES, BUT TERA HAD HER *OWN* DOCTORS AND HER *OWN* TOMB.

COMBINED WITH SPELLS AND MAGIC, SHE PROMISED TO RETURN ONE DAY. TERA ALWAYS KEPT HER PROMISES.

WONDERFUL PERFORMANCE FROM AN ACCOMPLISHED CON MAN.

STILL SMUGGLING, OR HAVE YOU MOVED UP INTO THEFT, CORBECK?

MR DOYLE. JOHN IS A GUEST WITHIN THIS HOUSE.

THAT'S ALRIGHT MARGARET. PHILLIP DOYLE AND I GO BACK A LONG TIME. WE HAVE AN UNDERSTANDING.

HE HATES ME AND I HAVE OTHER THINGS TO DO RATHER THAN *THINK* OF HIM.

LIKE SAVING ABEL'S LIFE.

AAAAHHHHHH!!!

LATER...

AGGGKKKKK

AKKKK-KKTT

AT THE STABLES.

NN@?$*NN

ROBERT AWOKE AND RUSHED TO FIND MARGARET.

MARGARET? WHAT ARE YOU DOING?

NN^`#NN

NN"!÷!#NN

IS SHE POSSESSED?

WE NEED TO GET HER BACK INSIDE!

WHAT LANGUAGE IS THAT?

ANCIENT EGYPTIAN.

OF ALL THE CONS, THIS IS THE CRAZIEST. MARGARET! A--AHHHHH!!!

GRIK!

MARGARET! LET DOYLE GO!

∿∿@?¿*∿∿

∿∿^`†#∿∿

THUMP!

AH, LISTEN TO THIS!

SHE'S TELLING US THAT SHE IS TERA, QUEEN OF THE EGYPTIANS, RULER OF THE NORTH AND SOUTH, DAUGHTER OF THE SUN!

URGGHH~

SHE'S INTRODUCING HERSELF IN THE MOST CUSTOMARY MANNER!

I KNOW WHERE THE RUBY IS, WHERE THE LAMPS ARE, ABEL'S PLAN, AND I KNOW WHAT YOU WANT, TERA.

I PROMISE YOU THAT YOU *SHALL HAVE IT!* TRUST ME.

UHHH... WHERE AM I?

YOU MUST TRUST JOHN CORBECK...

23

LATER...

ABEL'S BEEN PLANNING THIS FOR YEARS. HE CALLED IT THE "GREAT EXPERIMENT".

HE WANTED TO SEE IF THE LEGACY COULD BE FULFILLED. SO FOR YEARS WE COLLECTED EVERYTHING, THE JARS, LAMPS...

THE MUMMY?

YES, EVEN TERA HERSELF.

WE TOOK APART HER TOMB AND BROUGHT IT ALL HERE TO THE HOUSE.

ABEL STUDIED THE CHANGES IN THE STARS OF THE LAST FIVE THOUSAND YEARS AND SELECTED THIS AS THE PERFECT LOCATION FOR HIS EXPERIMENT.

WHAT WE'RE LOOKING FOR IS THE KEY TO THE TOMB. THE OBELISK.

AH! SHINE THE LIGHT HERE.

THIS IS A WASTE OF TIME, JOHN. THERE'S NOTHING HERE! LOOK!

TERA WAS NOT THE ONLY MUMMY WE BROUGHT BACK.

GAH!

THERE IT IS: THE KEY TO THE TOMB. SHE IS NOT GOING TO LET US GO UNTIL SHE GETS WHAT SHE WANTS.

SHE PLANNED TO RETURN WITH COMPANY, SO ABEL CUT UP HER COURT AND BURIED THEM HERE IN UNSANCTIFIED GROUND.

BACK IN ABEL TRELAWNEY'S STUDY.

THE KEY! WHERE IS IT?!

HASN'T BEEN THERE SINCE THE LAST ATTACK.

WELL, WE NEED THE *RUBY*, IT IS IN THE *SAFE*, AND TO SAVE ABEL'S LIFE WE NEED THAT *KEY*!

DURING MY TIME AS A POLICE OFFICER I MET A MAN WITH GREAT LOCK-PICKING ABILITIES. I LEARNT A FEW THINGS FROM HIM.

THERE'S A FALSE BACK TO THE SAFE... YES...

THE STAR RUBY!

ABEL, WE'RE MOVING EVERYTHING DOWN TO TERA'S TOMB.

IN THE TOMB, EVERYTHING WAS IN PLACE.

LET US BEGIN.

HOW MANY TIMES DO I HAVE TO SAY THAT I'M DOING PERFECTLY WELL?

WE'VE BEEN THROUGH SO MUCH, DADDY! I WANTED TO MAKE SURE.

THANK-YOU DAUGHTER. IF I WEREN'T FINE, I'D SAY SO. PROMISE.

GLAD TO HAVE YOU BACK, MR. TRELAWNEY!

ALL FIXED UP, SIR. I'M IN LOVE WITH YOUR DAUGHTER, SO I'D DO ANYTHING FOR HER.

IT'S GOOD TO BE BACK, ROBERT.

I WANT TO THANK YOU FOR EVERYTHING YOU HAVE DONE. HOW ARE YOU NOW?

I'M HAPPY TO HEAR THAT SON.

WE'LL BE BACK SOON. UNTIL THEN HERE IS THE *STAR RUBY*, I KNOW HOW MUCH IT MEANS TO YOU.

HAVE A SAFE TRIP AND GODSPEED.

DADDY! HELP ME!

VROOM!

MARGARET!!!

This edition first published in 2010 by
Franklin Watts
338 Euston Road
London NW1 3BH

Franklin Watts Australia
Level 17/207 Kent Street
Sydney NSW 2000

First published in the USA by Magic Wagon, a division of the ABDO Group

1 3 5 7 9 10 8 6 4 2

Based upon the works of Bram Stoker
Written by Bart A. Thompson
Illustrated by Brian Miroglio
Letters and colours by Lynx Studio
Edited and directed by Chazz DeMoss
Cover design by Neil Klinepier
UK cover design by Peter Scoulding

A CIP catalogue record for this book is available from the British Library.

Dewey number: 741.5

ISBN: 978 0 7496 9684 9

Printed in China

Franklin Watts is a division of Hachette Children's Books,
an Hachette UK company.
www.hachette.co.uk

READ THE REST OF THIS STORY IN: WEREWOLF